Seashore Sticke

Lisa Miles

Illustrated by John Barber, Trevor Boyer, Hilary Burn,
Alan Harris, Annabel Milne and Peter Stebbing

Edited by Simon Tudhope
Designed by Candice Whatmore
Consultant: Dr Margaret Rostron

How to use this book

There are over a hundred different plants and animals in this book.
Using the descriptions and the pictures, match each sticker to the right
animal or plant. If you need help, an index and checklist at the back
of the book tells you which sticker goes with which entry.

Different areas of the seashore are mentioned in this book.
The diagram below shows where they are.

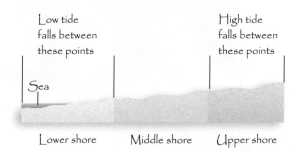

Low tide
falls between
these points

High tide
falls between
these points

Sea

Lower shore   Middle shore   Upper shore

Shells

Empty shells once grew on, and protected, the soft bodies of animals called molluscs. Some molluscs live on the shore; others live out at sea.

Dog whelk

Dog whelk

Dog whelks are common. Those that feed on barnacles turn white, while those that feed on mussels become coloured or striped. 3cm (1¼in)

WHEN ....

WHERE ....

Common whelk

Whelks are gastropods, which means they have a muscular foot that clings to rocks or seaweed. They live in the sea, but empty shells are found on beaches. 8cm (3in)

WHEN ....

WHERE ....

Common whelk

Common limpet

Limpets are gastropods, and clamp onto rocks. They feed on seaweed and are seen on rocky shores when tide is out. 7cm (2¾in)

WHEN ...... *Saturday*

WHERE ...... *Wales*

Common limpet

Blue-rayed limpet

Blue-rayed limpet

Lives on and eats oarweed. When young, the rays of dots on its shell are a bright, electric blue, but they fade as it gets older. 1.5cm (½in)

WHEN ....

WHERE ....

2

Common periwinkle

Seen close to the sea on all
kinds of shores. Feeds on
seaweed. 2.5cm (1in)

WHEN ....

WHERE ....

Common
periwinkle

Flat periwinkle

Looks like the lumpy air
pockets of the bladder
wrack seaweed it feeds
on. Yellow, orange or
brown. 1.5cm (½in)

WHEN ....

WHERE ....

Flat
periwinkle

European cowrie

Found on rocky shores in
Europe. Three dark patches
on its shell. 1.2cm (½in)

WHEN ....

WHERE ....

European
cowrie

Painted top shell

Lives on rocks and under stones. Yellow
or pink shell, with red stripes. 2.5cm (1in)

WHEN ....

WHERE ....

Painted
top shell

Pelican's foot shell

So named because
the edge of its shell
is shaped like a
webbed foot.
Quite rare, but
sometimes seen
on the shore.
5.5cm (2¼in)

WHEN ....

WHERE ....

Pelican's
foot shell

Necklace shell

Preys on other molluscs by drilling a
hole in their shell and eating the flesh
inside. Sandy shores. 4cm (1½in)

WHEN ....

WHERE ....

Necklace
shell

Two-shelled creatures

These molluscs are bivalves, which means they have two shells hinged together.

Saddle oyster

Sticks firmly to rocks. Shell often grows to fit rock's shape. Found on the middle shore. 6cm (2¼in)

WHEN ....

WHERE ....

Saddle oyster

Heart cockle

Heart cockle

Has a heart-shaped outline. Lives in muddy sand below the low tide level, but may be washed ashore. 9.5cm (3¾in)

WHEN ....

WHERE ....

Queen scallop

Swims by clapping its shells together like flippers, forcing water out behind to jet itself along. 4–5cm (1½–2in)

WHEN ....

WHERE ....

Queen scallop

Razor shell

Looks like an old-fashioned razor blade. Lives buried in sand or mud. The two shells are hinged at one end. 15cm (6in)

WHEN ....

WHERE ....

Razor shell

Common mussel

Common mussel

Blue or brown. Found on rocky shores and estuaries. Attaches itself to rock with thin threads. People collect this kind of mussel to eat. 7cm (2¾in)

WHEN ....

WHERE ....

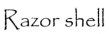

Soft-bodied creatures

These molluscs have no outer shells, though some have shells on the inside.

Common squid

Orange-clubbed sea slug

Common squid

Open sea; but inner shell (called a pen) is often washed up on the beach. 60cm (23in)

WHEN ....

WHERE ....

Orange-clubbed sea slug

Lives in shallow water. White with orange-tipped "clubs". Bright colour warns predators it tastes nasty. 2cm (¾in)

WHEN ....

WHERE ....

Common cuttlefish

Large, soft body surrounds a thick shell called a cuttlebone, which is often washed ashore. 30cm (12in)

WHEN ....

WHERE ....

Common cuttlefish

Common grey sea slug

Common grey sea slug

Common on rocky middle shores under stones. Feeds on sea anemones. 8cm (3in)

WHEN ....

WHERE ....

Curled octopus

Lives among rocks. Occasionally seen on extreme lower shore, when tide is far out. Colour can be yellow to reddish-brown. 20cm (8in)

WHEN ....

WHERE ....

Curled octopus

Crabs and their relatives

These creatures are crustaceans. They have shells and jointed legs.

Shore crab

Smooth, broad shell that varies from dark green to red. Very common on sandy and rocky shores. 4cm (1½in)

WHEN ....

WHERE ....

Shore crab

Velvet swimming crab

Eats other crabs. Found on the lower shore. Hairy shell, and flat back legs that help it swim. 8cm (3in)

WHEN ....

WHERE ....

Velvet swimming crab

Edible crab

Lives in deep water. Small ones seen in rock pools, or buried under sand on lower shore. Popular seafood. Up to 11.5cm (4½in)

WHEN ....

WHERE ....

Edible crab

Common hermit crab

Finds empty shells to live in. When it outgrows one shell, it looks for a larger one. Up to 10cm (4in)

WHEN ....

WHERE ....

Common hermit crab

Squat lobster

Actually a crab. Found under rocks and stones on the lower shore. Up to 6.5cm (2½in)

WHEN ....

WHERE ....

Squat lobster

Common lobster

Small ones sometimes found in rock pools, but most crawl along the seabed in deep water. Its strong claws give a nasty pinch. Up to 50cm (19¾in)

WHEN ....

WHERE ....

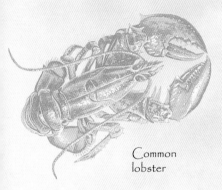

Common lobster

Acorn barnacle

Sticks to a rock and builds a hard shell around itself that has a diamond-shaped opening in the top. 1.5cm (½in)

WHEN ....

WHERE ....

Acorn barnacle

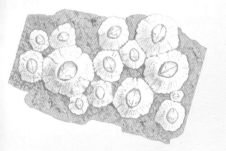

Common prawn

Common prawn

Common in shallow water, sometimes found in rock pools, too. Told from other prawns and shrimps by the sawteeth on its snout. 6.5cm (2½in)

WHEN ....

WHERE ....

Sea slater

Sea slater

Seen in breakwaters and rocks on upper shore. Feeds at night. 3cm (1¼in)

WHEN ....

WHERE ....

Common shrimp

Common in sandy estuaries. Has broad, flat claws on its front legs. People catch shrimps and prawns to eat. 5cm (2in)

Common shrimp

WHEN ....

WHERE ....

Flowers and grasses

Seashore plants are blasted by salty wind, so they grow low, with deep, tough roots.

Sea campion

Cliffs and shingle beaches. Spreads to form soft cushion on ground. 20cm (8in)

Sea campion

WHEN ....

WHERE ....

Yellow horned poppy

Grows on shingle. Has long, curved seed pods. 50–60cm (20–23½in)

WHEN ....

WHERE ....

Yellow horned poppy

Sea kale

Grows in clumps on shingle. Broad, fleshy leaves with crinkly edges. 1m (3¼ft)

WHEN ....

WHERE ....

Sea kale

Sea holly

Found on sand and shingle. Prickly grey-blue leaves turn white in winter. 50cm (19¾in)

WHEN ....

WHERE ....

Sea holly

Sea bindweed

Trails along ground, binding sand together. Thick, shiny leaves. 60cm (23½in)

WHEN ....

WHERE ....

Sea bindweed

Sea aster

Grows in saltmarshes, which are areas of sand and salty mud. Has mauve or white petals. 1m (3¼ft)

WHEN ....

WHERE ....

Sea aster

Bird's foot trefoil

Yellow flowers streaked with red. Seed pods split and curl when ripe. 10cm (4in)

WHEN ....

WHERE ....

Bird's foot trefoil

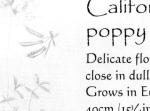

California poppy

Delicate flowers close in dull weather. Grows in Europe. 40cm (15¾in)

WHEN ....

WHERE ....

California poppy

Thrift

Marram grass

Grows in thick tufts on rocky beaches and cliffs. Particularly good at surviving salty spray. 15cm (6in)

WHEN ....

WHERE ....

Thrift

Marram grass

Grows on sand dunes. Long roots and leaves trap sand and stop it being blown away. 1.2m (4ft)

WHEN ....

WHERE ....

Sea lavender

Sea lavender

Tough saltmarsh plant. Its leaves grow in a clump close to the ground. 40cm (15¾in)

WHEN ....

WHERE ....

Sea couch grass

Just above high tide level. Long roots. Ridges of sand build up around it. 40cm (15¾in)

WHEN ....

WHERE ....

Sea couch grass

Cliff birds

Cormorant

During spring and early summer, many seabirds gather on cliffs to breed. They form huge, noisy groups and squabble for space on the rock ledges where they build their nests.

Cormorant

Seen mainly near the sea; sometimes on lakes. Wings not waterproof, so spreads them out to dry. 90cm (35½in)

WHEN ....

WHERE ....

Gannet

Dives headfirst from a great height into the sea to catch fish. Nests on rocky islands in messy nests. 90cm (35½in)

Gannet

WHEN ....

WHERE ....

Shag

Shag (male)

During breeding season, male grows crest, and feathers take on a green sheen. 76cm (30in)

WHEN ....

WHERE ....

Guillemot

Say "gilli-mot". Lays single egg straight onto the cliff ledge. The egg is pear-shaped, so that it spins when knocked and doesn't roll over the edge. 42cm (16½in)

WHEN ....

WHERE ....

Guillemot

Razorbill

Flat-sided beak. Nests in cracks in cliffs, or sometimes on ledges with guillemots. 40cm (15¾in)

WHEN ....

WHERE ....

Razorbill

Herring gull

Seen inland, as well as on coasts. Noisy bird. Nests on cliffs, buildings or the ground. Scavenges for food. 6ocm (23½in)

WHEN ....

WHERE ....

Herring gull

Great black-backed gull

Very large. 1.5m (5ft) wingspan. Sometimes eats other seabirds. Seen alone or in small groups. 7ocm (27½in)

WHEN ....

WHERE ....

Great black-backed gull

Puffin

Lives out at sea, except in breeding season. Colonies nest in holes on grassy cliff tops and islands. Stripy bill in summer. 3ocm (12in)

WHEN ....

WHERE ....

Puffin

Kittiwake

Spends most time out at sea, where it can be seen following ships. Its nest is made of green seaweed, and stuck to the cliff with mud and droppings. 45cm (17¾in)

WHEN ....

WHERE ....

Kittiwake

Fulmar

From a distance looks like a gull, except it glides on stiff wings, and flies with short wing beats. Spends most time out at sea. Nests on the highest cliff ledges. 45cm (17¾in)

WHEN ....

WHERE ....

Fulmar

Shore birds

You can see lots of different birds on the seashore, especially if it's a quiet stretch of coast.

Black-headed gull

Curlew

Curlew

Spends winter by the shore. Uses curved bill to dig deep down in the sand for lugworms. 48–64cm (19–25¼in)

WHEN ....

WHERE ....

Black-headed gull

Common. Often seen inland. Nests in colonies on marshes, dunes and shingle. Its head is dark only during summer. Red beak and legs. 38cm (15in)

WHEN ....

WHERE ....

Shelduck

Sheldrake (male)

Often nests in old rabbit holes in sand dunes. Eats molluscs. Male has knob on bill. 60cm (23½in)

WHEN ....

WHERE ....

Common tern

Ringed plover

Say "pluvver". Seen on sandy or shingle shores, and near estuaries in winter. 20cm (8in)

WHEN ....

WHERE ....

Ringed plover

Common tern

Nests in groups on beaches and sand dunes. Long wings and long tail feathers can easily be seen when it's in the air. Dives to catch small fish. 34cm (13½in)

WHEN ....

WHERE ....

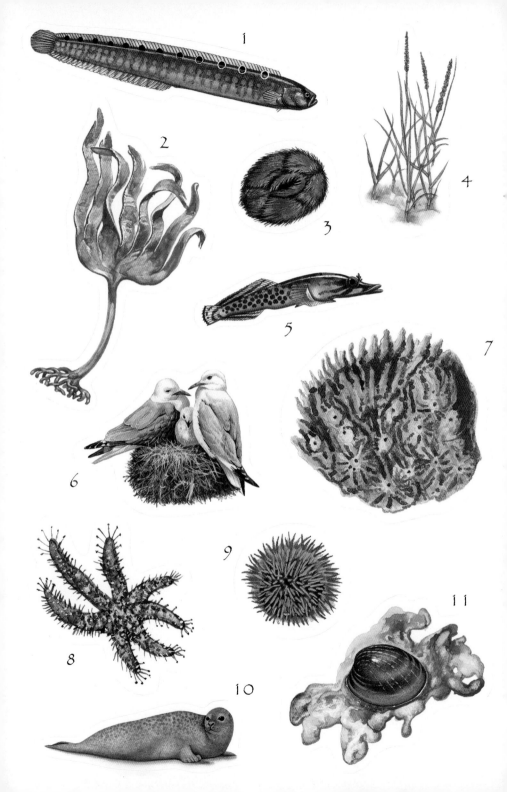

1

2

3

4

5

6

7

8

9

10

11

12

13

14

15

16

17

18

19

20

21

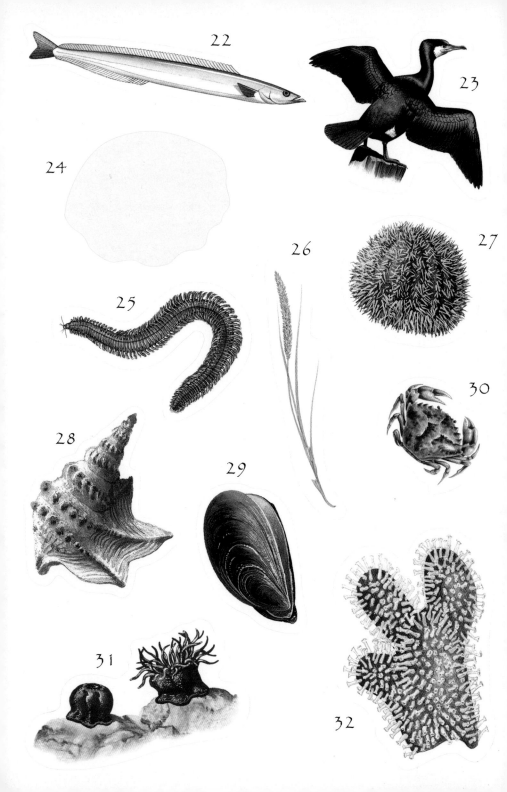

22

23

24

26

27

25

30

28

29

31

32

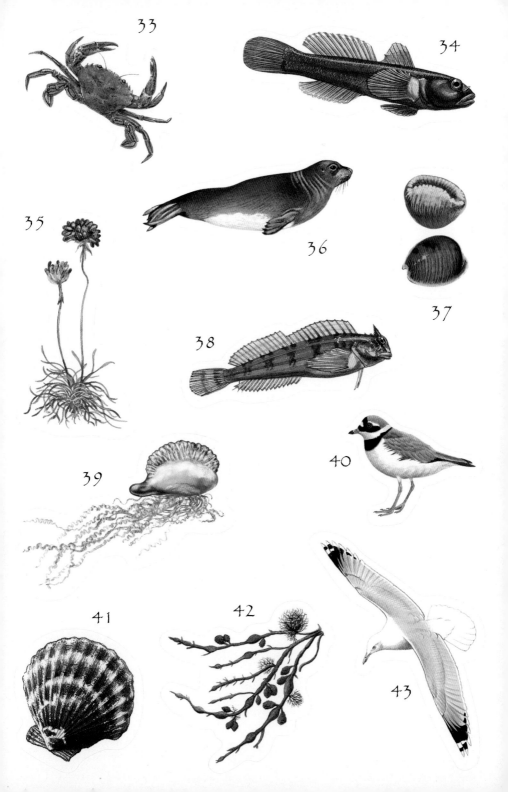

33

34

35

36

37

38

39

40

41

42

43

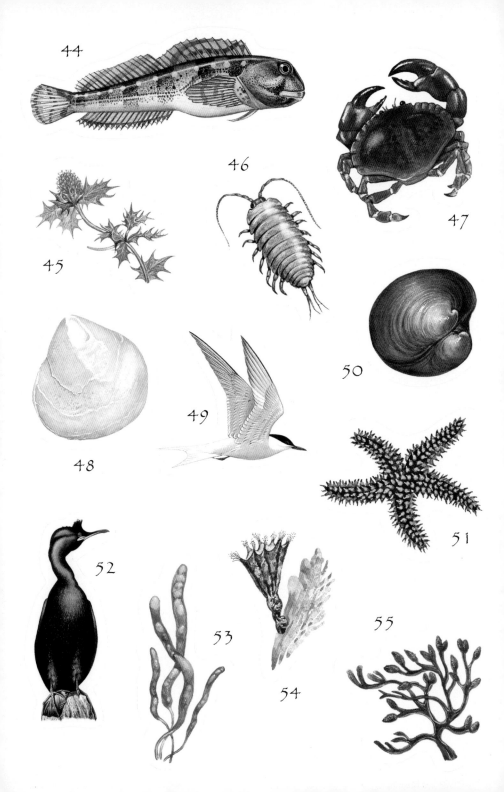

44

46

47

45

50

48

49

51

52

53

54

55

56

57

58

59

60

61

62

63

64

65

66

67

68

69

70

71

72

73

74

75

76

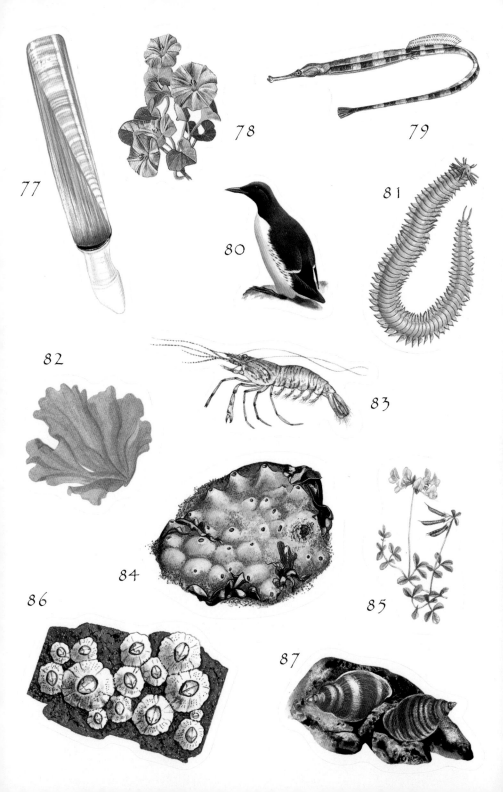

77

78

79

80

81

82

83

84

85

86

87

88

89

91

90

92

93

94

95

96

97

98

99

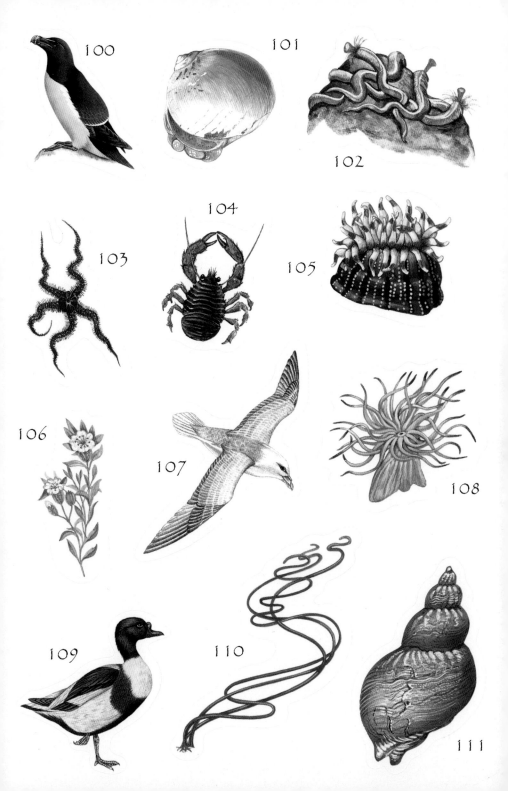

100

101

102

103

104

105

106

107

108

109

110

111

Mammals

Seals are the largest sea animals that live on the shore. Porpoises and dolphins live in the sea, but still need to come up for air.

Common seal

Common seal

Lives in herds on sandbanks in estuaries. Fast swimmer. Can stay underwater for half an hour. 1.8m (6ft)

WHEN ....

WHERE ....

Grey seal

Lives in small colonies on rocky shores. Rests on land at low tide and sunset, but sleeps in the sea. 2.9m (9½ft)

WHEN ....

WHERE ....

Grey seal

Common porpoise

Common porpoise

Small whale with blunt nose. Often swims near the coast in groups. Eats squid and fish. 1.8m (6ft)

WHEN ....

WHERE ....

Mediterranean monk seal

Very rare. Lives on small rocky beaches on islands. 2.4m (8ft)

WHEN ....

WHERE ....

Mediterranean monk seal

Common dolphin

Common dolphin

Fast swimmer. Lives in large groups. Very playful. Often jumps right out of the water. 2.4m (8ft)

WHEN ....

WHERE ....

Fishes

Some seashore fishes bury themselves in sand at low tide. Others live in rock pools.

Sand eel

Sand eel

These fish live in huge groups, called schools, close to the sea bottom in shallow water. They burrow headfirst into the sand. 20cm (8in)

WHEN ....

WHERE ....

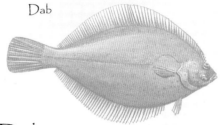

Dab

Dab

Seen in shallow water on muddy or sandy bottoms. Eyes on one side of head. Eats little crustaceans. 25cm (10in)

WHEN ....

WHERE ....

Corkwing wrasse

Starts life female but may become male later. Eats animals with shells. Lives in shallow water. 25cm (10in)

WHEN ....

WHERE ....

Corkwing wrasse (male)

Butterfish

Greater pipefish

On muddy or sandy bottoms. Eats young fish and tiny crustaceans. Hides in seaweed or eel grass. 45cm (17¾in)

WHEN ....

WHERE ....

Greater pipefish

Butterfish

Lives in cool water. Slippery. Slides between rocks. Also seen under seaweed and stones. 25cm (10in)

WHEN ....

WHERE ....

Sea scorpion

Lives in pools on the shore and among seaweed. Eats shrimps, small crabs, and other fish. 17cm (6¾in)

WHEN ....

WHERE ....

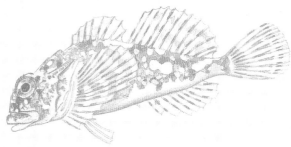

Sea scorpion

Montagu's blenny

Lives in rock pools. Eats acorn barnacles when they poke out of their shell. 8cm (3in)

WHEN ....

WHERE ....

Shore clingfish

Shore clingfish

Lives under rocks, clinging on with a sucker fin. Colour varies from pink to green. In the summer, pairs of clingfish guard their eggs. 6.5cm (2½in)

WHEN ....

WHERE ....

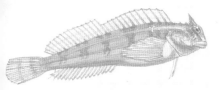

Montagu's blenny

Shanny

Lives in seaweed in pools on rocky and sandy shores. Changes skin colour from grey to brown or green to match its surroundings. Eats crustaceans. 16cm (6¼in)

WHEN ....

WHERE ....

Rock goby

Rock goby

Lives on rocky shores, in pools and under stones. Eyes on top of its head, to keep a look out for predators. 12cm (4¾in)

WHEN ....

WHERE ....

Shanny

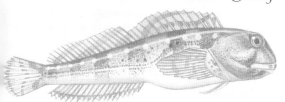

15

Jellyfishes and their relatives

These jelly-like creatures get washed up on shore. Don't touch them – many have stinging tentacles.

Lion's mane jellyfish

The world's largest jellyfish. Stinging tentacles trail up to 30m (100ft) in length. Body up to 2m (6½ft) wide.

WHEN ....

WHERE ....

Lion's mane jellyfish

Moon jellyfish

Moon jellyfish

Common and harmless. Transparent with purple rim, and four pale purple rings in the middle. Body 15cm (6in) wide.

WHEN ....

WHERE ....

Portuguese man-o'-war

Not a true jellyfish. Can't swim, just floats. All its tentacles are separate creatures, living as a colony. Painful sting. Body 15cm (6in) wide.

WHEN ....

WHERE ....

Portuguese man-o'-war

Stalked jellyfish

Harmless. Attaches itself to seaweed on shore. Funnel-shaped body has tentacles around its rim. 2.5cm (1in)

WHEN ....

WHERE ....

Stalked jellyfish

Sea gooseberry

Sea gooseberry

Distant relative of jellyfish. Size of a gooseberry. Traps food in two sticky tentacles. Body 1cm (½in) wide.

WHEN ....

WHERE ....

Worms

Seashore worms are related to earthworms. Some live in tubes of sand, some burrow, and some wriggle along the surface.

Keelworm

Keelworm

Lives on rocks, stones or empty shells on the seashore in a hard, white tube with a ridge along the top. Males have yellow bodies; females are violet. 3cm (1¼in)

WHEN ....

WHERE ....

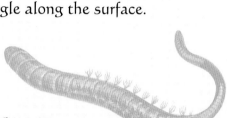

Lugworm

Burrows underground. Sucks in sand, digests it, then passes it out, leaving spaghetti-like sandcasts on the surface. 15cm (6in)

Lugworm

WHEN ....

WHERE ....

Sea mouse

Sea mouse (underside)

Bristles on back make it look a bit like a mouse. Side-bristles glint with many colours. 10cm (4in)

WHEN ....

WHERE ....

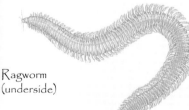

Ragworm (underside)

Ragworm

Digs a burrow in sand and mud, in which it spins a sticky net to catch food. Has a red line down its back. 10cm (4in)

WHEN ....

WHERE ....

Green leaf worm

Green leaf worm

Crawls among barnacles and under seaweed on rocks, or hides in rock crevices. 10cm (4in)

WHEN ....

WHERE ....

Starfishes and their relatives

These animals all have prickly skin, and a mouth on the underside of their body.

Common sunstar

Common sunstar

Often beautifully patterned.
Up to fourteen arms.
Eats other starfishes.
4–8cm (1½–3in)

WHEN ....

WHERE ....

Common
starfish

Common starfish

Like most starfishes, has five arms. If one arm breaks off, a new one can grow. Uses its rows of suckers to climb up rocks. 5–10cm (2–4in)

WHEN ....

WHERE ....

Spiny starfish

Sharp spikes for defence.
Lives on low shore, and in deep water. 8–12cm (3–4¾in)

WHEN ....

WHERE ....

Spiny
starfish

Cushion star

Very small starfish with short arms. Lives under stones, often in rock pools. Up to 2cm (¾in)

WHEN ....

WHERE ....

Mediterranean multi-armed starfish

Six to nine arms, of different lengths. Lives on Mediterranean coasts. 8–12cm (3–4¾in)

WHEN ....

WHERE ....

Mediterranean
multi-armed starfish

Cushion
star

Brown serpent star

Prefers to live in warm waters, such as the Mediterranean Sea. Its stripes darken with age. 10–15cm (4–6in)

WHEN ....

WHERE ....

Common brittle star

Lives under stones in rock pools. Arms break easily. 3–8cm (1¼–3in)

WHEN ....

WHERE ....

Common brittle star

Brown serpent star

Edible sea urchin

Black sea urchin

Black spines. Found on lower shore and in deep water, not around Britain. 6–10cm (2¼–4in)

WHEN ....

WHERE ....

Edible sea urchin

Scrapes algae off rocks with teeth on the base of its body. Eaten in many countries. 15cm (6in)

WHEN ....

WHERE ....

Black sea urchin

Purple-tipped sea urchin

Lives under rocks on lower shore. Spines have purple tips. More common than edible sea urchin. 4cm (1½in)

WHEN ....

WHERE ....

Purple-tipped sea urchin

Sea potato

Lives in sand at the lowest tide level. Leaves a dent where it has burrowed. 5–6cm (2–2¼in)

WHEN ....

WHERE ....

Sea potato

Some other sea creatures

Sea anemones, sponges and coral are all animals, even though they look like flowers. They're mostly seen on underwater rocks.

Dahlia
anemone

Plumose anemone

Orange or white. Often seen just below the water's surface on pier supports. 20cm (8in) wide.

WHEN ....

WHERE ....

Dahlia anemone

Many different colours. Hard to spot because body often covered with piec of shell. 6–7cm (2¼–2¾in) wide.

WHEN ....

WHERE ....

Plumose
anemone

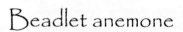

Beadlet anemone

Red or green with blue spots, and thin blue line around base. Lives in rock pools. 3cm (1¼in) wide.

WHEN ....

WHERE ....

Beadlet
anemone

Snakelocks
anemone

Snakelocks anemone

Grey or green. Sticky tentacles contract when touched, but do not disappear. Lives on rocky shores. 6–7cm (2¼–2¾in) wide.

WHEN ....

WHERE ....

Purse sponge

Hangs down in groups under rocks, in pools and among seaweeds. Out of water, collapses into a purse shape. 1–2cm ($\frac{1}{2}$–$\frac{3}{4}$in) wide.

WHEN ....

WHERE ....

Purse sponge

Encrusting sponge

Forms crusts over rocks. Has many small openings all over its surface. 50cm (19$\frac{3}{4}$in) wide.

WHEN ....

WHERE .... Encrusting sponge

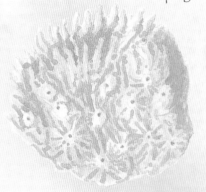

Breadcrumb sponge

Grows on rocks and seaweeds. Many different shapes. Colour varies from green to yellow. 10cm (4in) wide.

WHEN ....

WHERE ....

Breadcrumb sponge

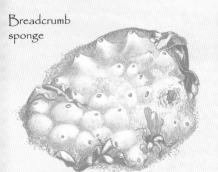

Dead men's fingers coral

Tiny creatures that live together in a hand-shaped colony. White, pink or yellow. Grows offshore in cool water. Sometimes seen washed up on beach. 20cm (8in) high.

WHEN ....

WHERE ....

Dead men's fingers coral

Seaweed

Some seaweeds grow
on rocky coasts. Other,
deep-water, seaweeds are
often washed ashore.

Knotted
wrack

Sea lace

Sea
lace

Very long, thin cords
wave about in underwater
currents. Lives in shallow
water. Up to 6m (19³/₄ft)

WHEN ....

WHERE ....

Knotted wrack

Lives on sheltered rocks
on the middle shore.
Tufts of red seaweed
grow on it. 1m (3¹/₄ft)

WHEN ....

WHERE ....

Bladder wrack

Pairs of bladders (pockets
of air) keep it upright in the
water. Has a large holdfast to
keep it anchored. 60cm (24in)

WHEN ....

WHERE ....

Bladder
wrack

Sea lettuce

Found on all types
of shore. Gets darker
with age. 20cm (8in)

WHEN ....

WHERE ....

Sea lettuce

Channel
wrack

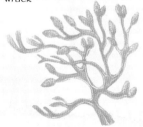

Channel wrack

Sides curve together
to form grooves. Look
for it on the upper
shore. 10cm (4in)

WHEN ....

WHERE ....

Sea oak

Delicate. Pale crimson.
Common in rock pools
on the lower shore.
Up to 15cm (6in)

WHEN ....

WHERE ....

Sea oak

Oarweed

Edible dulse

Lives underwater in deep
rock pools. Up to 30cm (12in)

WHEN ....

WHERE ....

Oarweed

Divided into strap-like
branches. Seen on rocks
in shallow water. 1.5m (5ft)

WHEN ....

WHERE ....

Edible
dulse

Eel grass

Sea grass, not seaweed. Grows
in large banks in estuaries and
sheltered coasts. 1m (3¼ft)

WHEN ....

WHERE ....

Gut laver

Looks a bit like
intestines. Common.
Found in rock pools
on the upper shore.
20cm (8in)

WHEN ....

WHERE ....

Eel grass

Gut
laver

Index and checklist

This list will help you find every animal and plant in the book. The first number after each entry tells you which page it's on. The second one (in brackets) is the number of the sticker.

Additional design: Marc Maynard
Cover design: Kate Rimmer
Digital imaging: Keith Furnival

Cover images: © D Hurst / Alamy, Celia Mannings / Alamy, Rex Argent / Alamy and Purestock / Alamy

This edition first published in 2010 by Usborne Publishing Ltd, Usborne House, 83–85 Saffron Hill, London ECIN 8RT, England. www.usborne.com Copyright © 2010, 1978 Usborne Publishing Ltd. The name Usborne and the devices ♀♕ are Trade Marks of Usborne Publishing Ltd. All rights reserved. No part of this publication may be reproduced, stored in a retrieval system, or transmitted in any form or by any means, electronic, mechanical, photocopying, recording or otherwise, without the prior permission of the publisher. Printed in Heshan, Guangdong, China.